Animal An

The following animals are hiding

Ringo the Flamingo

I'm a pink flamingo
Life just isn't fair
What's the point of legs
When I don't get to use the pair?

I'm trying to keep my balance
It's not a lot of fun
I keep on toppling over
As my leg's stuck up my bum

My beak is bent and wonky
So now I'm in a mood
The other birds are laughing
I think they're very rude

Ola the Polar Bear

I'm a little polar bear
I'm really not that old
I need some woolly socks
Because my feet are always cold

My mother says I'm silly
She says my feet will grow
How's that going to help me?
They'll still be stuck in snow

I thought I'd solved the problem
I tried standing on my head
It didn't seem to work
Because my ears got cold instead

Millard the Monkey

I'm a little monkey
I'm sitting in the zoo
I'm showing you my bottom
As there's nothing else to do

My keeper says I'm naughty
I'm showing too much cheek
But he's the one who's naughty
He doesn't have to peek

Look, here comes my girlfriend
She's such a little charmer
And if she gets much closer
I'll be sharing my banana

Calamity the Crocodile

I'm a little crocodile,
I made a big mistake
I went off to the dentist
As my teeth began to ache

The dentist sat me in his chair
He said 'please open wide'
But OOPS he lost his balance
And he ended up inside

The dental nurse is very cross
She says I can't come back
It's such a lot of fuss to make
...for such a tiny snack

Antony the Ant Eater

I'm a little ant eater,
It's really not my day
It's time to have my breakfast
But the ants have run away

I don't like being an ant eater
It's not a job I chose
Ants are very wriggly
They send tickles up my nose

Sometimes I eat five or six
Or maybe nine or ten
But it only takes a single sneeze
To make me start again

AAAASHOO!!
ANT HILL
TISSUES

Polly the Poodle

I'm a little poodle
There's sadness in my world
I wanted sleek and shiny hair
But all I got were curls

There's more as I get older
That's how it seems to me
I'm finding curls in places
Where they never used to be

I need to get some straighteners
But where would I begin?
With four big clumsy paws like mine
How would I plug them in?

Moo-riel the Cow

I'm a grumpy dairy cow
My farmer doesn't care
Although he milks me every day
I never get my share

I dream of strawberry milkshake
And steaming cups of tea
I'd love to make a custard
But that will never be

The farmer should be careful
Next time we're in the shed
I think he might just end up
With a cow pat on his head

MOO-RIEL

Barney the Bee

I'm a little bumble bee
Been flying round for hours
Wearing stripy jumpers
Doing naughty stuff to flowers

I charm them with my friendly smile
We have a cosy chat
Then if they look away
I stuff their pollen in my sack

Sometimes they get nosey
They ask about my honey
But I fly away quite quickly
If they ask me for some money

SWAG

Romero the Rabbit

I'm a little rabbit
I'm feeling very stroppy
I want my ears to stand up straight
Instead, they're limp and floppy

The doctor gave me tablets
My ears sprang into life
I hopped off to the forest
To find myself a wife

I met a lovely rabbit
We scampered down the lane
But now I'm sitting crying
As my ears are limp again

Peter the Cheetah

I'm a little cheetah
I'm feeling most unwell
I think I have the measles
But it's difficult to tell

The doctor is quite worried
I might have an infection
He says he wants to visit me
To give me an injection

The doctor doesn't realise
That this will never be
As even when I'm poorly
He can't run as fast as me

Hogan the Hamster

I'm a breathless hamster
I'm always keeping fit
I run around my wheel each day
But don't have any kit

I don't have nice posh trainers
Nor snazzy running vest
It feels a bit embarrassing
To run around undressed

I need some tiny running shorts
They won't cost much to buy
Don't stare into my cage like that
I'm very very shy

HAMSTER
GEAR

Garth the Giraffe

I'm a very small giraffe
I'm trembling with the fright
I just peered at the ground today
And found I'm scared of heights

I know there's something wrong with me
As someone's placed my toes
A little bit too far away
From both my ears and nose

It's breezy when you're very tall
I don't like chilly weather
I'm trying to knit a winter scarf
It's taking me forever

Dale the Whale

I'm a chubby ocean whale
I'm feeling so irate
Despite a diet of fish it seems
I always put on weight

I don't eat jammy dodgers
Or steak and kidney pie
I broke my bathroom scales last week
Which makes me want to cry

I do a lot of exercise
Go swimming every day
So can somebody please tell me
How I've ended up this way

Clawdia the Cat

I'm a little pussy cat
I'm sitting with a pout
It's very cold and wet outside
You want me to go out?

I haven't any welly boots
I haven't any mittens
And if I mix with other cats
I think I might have kittens

My whiskers will get soggy
In all the damp and fog
Don't push me out the cat flap
It's raining cats and dogs

Pee Pee the Panda

I'm a little panda
I'm feeling sad and blue
I'm told I need a girlfriend
But I'd rather eat bamboo

They've palmed me off with Chi Chi
She really is a pain
She's come all the way from China
She can go straight back again

She's bossy and she's smelly
Her markings are a fright
Us pandas are particular
It's not just black and white

PANDA
TO YOU!
BAMBOO
MONTHLY

Seymour the Squirrel

I'm a little squirrel
I've had a dreadful day
I've noticed with a shock
That all my nuts are on display

Some are smooth and shiny
Some are large and red
I need to put my paws on them
And cover up my spread

I don't know how it happened
I really don't know when
But if you turn your back
Then I can hide them once again

Boris the Bat

I'm a little night time bat
I'm wearing such a frown
It's hard to have a tinkle
When you're hanging upside down

I never seem to plan too well
I'm always in a muddle
My feet are high and dry
But now my ears are in a puddle

I wish it didn't happen
It's always a surprise
If I'd known that it was coming
I would have shut my eyes

Animal Angst

The animals have disappeared
They've all turned tail and fled
Perhaps they've gone out shopping
Or perhaps they've gone to bed
Perhaps they're cooking dinner
Or making brand new friends
Whatever they are doing
It seems you've reached the end

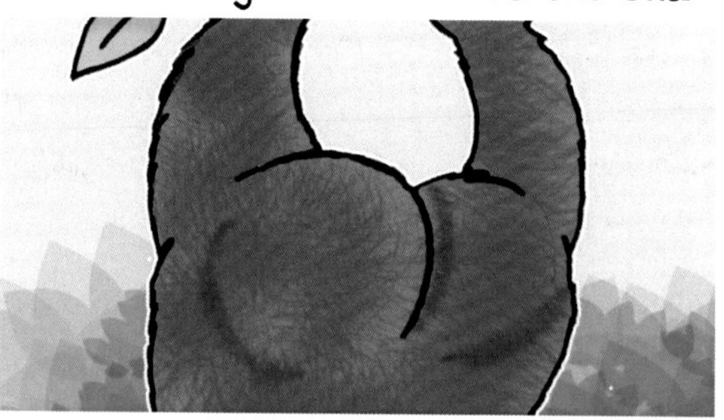